The Business of Certification Toolkit

21 Easy-to-Use Worksheets to Help You Build Your Certification Program

Lenora G. Knapp, Ph.D.

Joan E. Knapp, Ph.D.

Washington, DC

Information in this book is accurate as of the time of publication and consistent with standards of good practice in the general management community. As research and practice advance, however, standards may change. For this reason, it is recommended that readers evaluate the applicability of any recommendation in light of particular situations and changing standards.

American Society of Association Executives
1575 I Street, NW
Washington, DC 20005-1103
Phone: (888) 950-2723
Fax: (202) 408-9634
E-mail: books@asaenet.org

ASAE's core purpose is to advance the value of voluntary associations to society and to support the professionalism of the individuals who lead them.

Susan Robertson, Vice President, Marketing and Communications
Anna Nunan, Director of Book Publishing
Louise Quinn, Acquisitions Coordinator
Jennifer Moon, Production Manager
Anthony Conley, Operations Coordinator

Edited by Jody K. Vilschick

Cover design by John Hubbard and interior design by Black Dot Group

This book is available at a special discount when ordered in bulk quantities. For information, contact the ASAE Member Service Center at (202) 371-0940.

A complete catalog of titles is available on the ASAE Web site at www.asaenet.org/bookstore

Copyright © 2002 by the American Society of Association Executives

Permission to reproduce or transmit in any form or by any means, electronic or mechanical, including photocopying and recording, or by an information storage and retrieval system, must be obtained in writing from the director of book publishing or the publisher at the address or fax number above.

Printed in the United States of America.

10 9 8 7 6 5 4 3 2 1

Worksheet 1

Identifying Competitors

List the offerings that your program competes against in each of the following product categories.

PRODUCT CATEGORY	COMPETITOR'S OFFERING
Full-scale generalist certification	
Full-scale specialty/subspecialty certification	
Curriculum-based certificate	
Employer-sponsored in-house credential	
Certificates of attendance	
Academic degree programs	
Professional development programs	
Continuing education programs	

Worksheet 2

Developing a Competitor Profile

The competitor profile provides an overview of your competitors and the nature of their business. Use this worksheet to organize competitor data as it is collected. Complete a separate worksheet for each competitor.

Products/Services Provided

List the products and services offered by the competitor and next to these, list similar products/services offered (or under consideration) by your program. Rate the degree similarity between your products/services and those of the competitor using the following scale:

1 Low

2 Moderate

3 High

COMPETITOR'S PRODUCT/SERVICE	YOUR PRODUCT/SERVICE	SIMILARITY

Market Served

List the market segment(s) the competitor has targeted and specify the size of the competitor's business (in dollars and/or number of customers). In the last column, indicate the degree to which the segment overlaps one that you are targeting (i.e., completely, partially, or not at all).

MARKET SEGMENT	SIZE OF BUSINESS	OVERLAP

Worksheet 2

Developing a Competitor Profile (cont'd)

Culture/History/Goals

What is the culture within the organization (e.g., conservative, trend setting)?

In general, what are the organization's strategic goals and its motivations?

Why is the organization providing the competing products?

Has the organization been successful in launching new products/services?

Does the organization respond quickly and aggressively to industry trends and competitor's moves?

— continued

Worksheet 2

Developing a Competitor Profile (cont'd)

What is the organization's history within the certification/professional development market?

What factors might limit the organization's ability to take certain competitive actions (e.g., entrenched policies, "sacred cow" products)?

Perceptions and Assumptions

How does the organization perceive itself (e.g., technology leader, leading voice of the industry) and the marketplace (e.g., thriving, contracting)?

Under what assumptions does the organization operate?

Worksheet 2

Developing a Competitor Profile (cont'd)

Competitive Strategy

On what basis does the organization compete (e.g., price, convenient access, value-added)?

Financial Resources

How much income does the organization generate?

How much income does the product/service generate?

Are the competitive products/services subsidized by the organization and to what degree?

Are the products/services supported by outside funding from other entities and to what degree?

Worksheet 3

Analyzing Competitive Opportunities and Threats

Competitive Opportunities

List below the needs of the target market. Beside each need, identify the current market offerings designed to meet these needs. If any gaps exist between the offerings and customer needs, describe new products/services that might close these gaps. Or, if the current offerings are not effectively meeting customers' needs, list new products/services/features that might better serve the target market. Complete a separate worksheet for each target segment.

CUSTOMER NEED	MARKET OFFERINGS	NEW PRODUCTS/SERVICES

Competitive Threats

Identify competitive threats to the certification program. Next to each threat identified, list strategies that could be used to reduce the impact of this threat.

COMPETITIVE THREAT	STRATEGIES FOR REDUCING THREAT

Worksheet 4

Analyzing Competitive Strengths and Weaknesses

In the worksheet below, outline the competitive strengths and weaknesses for your program as well as those for each of your competitors.

	YOUR PROGRAM	COMPETITOR 1:	COMPETITOR 2:	COMPETITOR 3:
Strengths				
Weaknesses				

Worksheet 5

Formulating the Mission

Answer the questions below and use the responses to guide you in developing the mission statement.

What customer needs is the professional certification program trying to meet (e.g., recognition, credibility, prestige, job promotion, increase in salary, competitive advantage)?

What is the ultimate purpose of the program (e.g., to elevate the status of the profession, to provide employers with competent workers, protection of the public)?

For whom is the program designed (e.g., candidates, employers, specialists in a specific area)?

How does the program fulfill its purpose? What types of activities does it carry out? (Consider both technical functions and efforts to build stakeholder value.)

Worksheet 5

Formulating the Mission (cont'd)

How is the program unique as compared to other credentialing or professional development programs?

Craft a mission statement incorporating your answers to the above questions.

Worksheet 6

Identifying Environmental Opportunities and Threats

List the external factors that might impact (or are already impacting) your certification program and next to each factor, describe the opportunities and/or threats presented by the factor. Using the rating scales below, rate each factor as to the likelihood of occurrence and degree of impact on the program.

Likelihood of Occurrence

1 Not very likely to occur
2 Reasonably likely to occur
3 Very likely to occur
4 Currently occurring

Degree of Impact

1 Minor
2 Moderate
3 Very significant

Social Factors

FACTOR	OPPORTUNITY	THREAT	LIKELIHOOD	IMPACT

Political/Governmental Factors

FACTOR	OPPORTUNITY	THREAT	LIKELIHOOD	IMPACT

Worksheet 6

Identifying Environmental Opportunities and Threats (cont'd)

Economic Factors

FACTOR	OPPORTUNITY	THREAT	LIKELIHOOD	IMPACT

Technological Factors

FACTOR	OPPORTUNITY	THREAT	LIKELIHOOD	IMPACT

Worksheet 7

Identifying Internal Strengths and Weaknesses

Assess your organization's strengths and weaknesses with respect to each of the following areas. Extra space has been provided to add other dimensions relevant to your program.

	STRENGTH	WEAKNESS
Visibility		
Credibility/status		
Branding		
Organizational changes (e.g., department restructuring)		
Staff		
Volunteers		
Office space and equipment		
Program vendors and consultants		
Relationships with other entities		
Level of support within organization/industry		
Financial resources		

Worksheet 8

Formulating Strategic Goals, Tactics, and Critical Success Indicators

Formulating Goals

Review the program's mission statement (Worksheet 5) and identify what strategic goals must be met in order for the program to fulfill its mission. When selecting the goals, keep in mind the results of the environmental scan (Worksheet 6) and your analysis of the organization's internal strengths and weaknesses (Worksheet 7). List the strategic goals below.

Goal 1

____

____

Goal 2

____

____

Goal 3

____

____

Goal 4

____

____

Goal 5

____

____

Goal 6

____

____

— continued

Worksheet 8

Formulating Strategic Goals, Tactics, and Critical Success Indicators (cont'd)

Devising Tactics and Critical Success Indicators

In each matrix below, fill in the strategic goal on the top line and then list the tactics that will be used to accomplish the goal. For each tactic identified, specify under the heading, "Critical Success Indicator," how the tactic's effectiveness will be measured.

Goal:

TACTIC	CRITICAL SUCCESS INDICATOR
1.	
2.	
3.	
4.	
5.	
6.	
7.	
8.	

Worksheet 9

Strategic Plan Checklist

After you have prepared a draft strategic plan, review the document to ensure that it answers the following questions.

Mission

- What customer needs is the professional certification program trying to meet?
- What is the ultimate purpose of the program?
- For whom is the program designed?
- How does the program fulfill its purpose?
- How is the program unique as compared to other credentialing or professional development programs?

Strategic Goals

- What are the strategic goals of the program?
- How do the goals relate to the program's mission?

Strategic Tactics

- What tactics will be used to accomplish each strategic goal?

Critical Success Indicators

- What quantifiable measures will be used to evaluate the effectiveness of the tactics?
- What performance targets have been set for each tactic?
- Within what time frame must the performance target be met?

Worksheet 10

Understanding the Target Market

In the worksheet below, fill in the data you have gathered about your target market(s). We have listed the types of data that might be helpful in understanding candidate/certificant and employer customers and have included additional lines for you to add other data relevant to your particular target markets. Complete a separate worksheet for each market segment you are targeting.

CANDIDATES/CERTIFICANTS	
Age	______________________
Type of training/education	______________________
Years in the profession	______________________
Primary professional functions	______________________ ______________________
Work setting	______________________ ______________________
Other credentials/professional affiliations	______________________ ______________________
Geographic region	______________________
Motivations re: certification	______________________ ______________________
Needs	______________________ ______________________
Other	______________________ ______________________ ______________________

Worksheet 10

Understanding the Target Market (cont'd)

EMPLOYERS	
Number of employees	______________________
Annual revenue	______________________
Market in which business operates	______________________
Product/service mix	______________________ ______________________
Type of customer served	______________________ ______________________
Number of customers served annually	______________________
Motivations re: certification	______________________ ______________________
Needs	______________________ ______________________
Other	______________________ ______________________ ______________________ ______________________ ______________________ ______________________

Worksheet 11

Selecting a Positioning Strategy

Identifying the Distinctive Characteristics of the Program

The first step in determining how to position the certification program is to identify what it has to offer. The following questions will help you with this process. If you have more than one target market segment, complete a separate worksheet for each segment.

What makes the program distinctive and unique (in the eyes of the target market)?

How does the program's distinctive and unique features meet the target market's needs?

How does the program provide a greater value than its competitors?

Worksheet 11

Selecting a Positioning Strategy (cont'd)

Listed below are different types of positioning strategies. Based on your responses to the preceding questions, evaluate each strategy along the following dimensions:

- *Feasibility.* The degree to which: (a) the organization's constellation of strengths and weaknesses supports the implementation of the strategy and (b) the strategy is one that can be sustained profitably over the long term.
- *Ability to compel.* The degree to which the strategy will be a compelling one, given the characteristics of the target market.
- *Effectiveness vis-à-vis competitors.* The likelihood that the strategy will be effective given the state of competition within the marketplace.

Use the following scale to rate each strategy along each of the three dimensions:

1 Low

2 Moderate

3 High

EMPHASIS OF POSITIONING STRATEGY	FEASIBILITY	ABILITY TO COMPEL	EFFECTIVENESS
Program features	________	________	________
Benefits offered	________	________	________
Role in professional development	________	________	________
Distinctiveness vis-à-vis competitor	________	________	________
Product class	________	________	________

Worksheet 12

Identifying Marketing Strategies

Marketing strategies are implemented to support the positioning strategy (and thus create the desired image for the program) or achieve other business goals, such as increasing volumes and customer satisfaction. The strategies you select will be based on the results of your situational analysis. Use this worksheet to list the marketing opportunities and threats identified during your situational analysis and outline marketing strategies to address these situations. Rate the feasibility of each strategy, given your organization's constellation of strengths and weaknesses, using the following scale:

1 Low

2 Moderate

3 High

Worksheet 12

Identifying Marketing Strategies (cont'd)

Marketing Opportunities

Below outline the marketing opportunities you have identified and strategies that could be used to take capitalize on these opportunities. Rate the feasibility of each strategy.

OPPORTUNITY	STRATEGIES	FEASIBILITY
1. ______________	______________	______
______________	______________	______
	______________	______
	______________	______
2. ______________	______________	______
______________	______________	______
	______________	______
	______________	______
3. ______________	______________	______
______________	______________	______
	______________	______
	______________	______
4. ______________	______________	______
______________	______________	______
	______________	______
	______________	______
5. ______________	______________	______
______________	______________	______
	______________	______
	______________	______
6. ______________	______________	______
______________	______________	______
	______________	______
	______________	______

— continued

Worksheet 12

Identifying Marketing Strategies (cont'd)

Marketing Threats

Below outline the marketing threats you have identified and strategies that could be used to minimize or eliminate these threats. Rate the feasibility of each strategy.

THREATS	STRATEGIES	FEASIBILITY
1. ______	______	______
______	______	______
	______	______
	______	______
2. ______	______	______
______	______	______
	______	______
	______	______
3. ______	______	______
______	______	______
	______	______
	______	______
4. ______	______	______
______	______	______
	______	______
	______	______
5. ______	______	______
______	______	______
	______	______
	______	______
6. ______	______	______
______	______	______
	______	______
	______	______

Worksheet 13

Identifying Tactics for Implementing Marketing Strategy

This worksheet outlines a variety of tactics that can be used to support the marketing strategies you have selected. For each tactic, we have included one or more questions that should be considered. Answering these questions will help you to refine your tactics.

PRODUCT/SERVICE TACTICS

Features/Benefits

What distinctive features/benefits will be highlighted?

What existing features/benefits should be enhanced and in what way?

What new products/services should be added to existing offerings?

— continued

Worksheet 13

Identifying Tactics for Implementing Marketing Strategy (cont'd)

Pricing

What pricing tactics will be used (e.g., image pricing, value pricing)?

Packaging

What image is to be conveyed through packaging?

What approaches will be used to establish this image?

Worksheet 13

Identifying Tactics for Implementing Marketing Strategy (cont'd)

COMMUNICATION TACTICS

Advertising

Where will the program advertise?

What message will be conveyed in the advertisement?

Public Appearances

At what venues will appearances be made?

— continued

Worksheet 13

Identifying Tactics for Implementing Marketing Strategy (cont'd)

What form will the appearance take (e.g., presentation, exhibit hall booth)?

What message will be conveyed at each appearance?

Publicity

What types of events will be publicized?

What events will be created to encourage publicity?

Worksheet 13

Identifying Tactics for Implementing Marketing Strategy (cont'd)

Through what vehicles will these events be publicized?

What message will be conveyed with each form of publicity?

Direct Mail

What types of direct mail will be used?

What is the purpose of each mailing?

— continued

Worksheet 13

Identifying Tactics for Implementing Marketing Strategy (cont'd)

What message will be conveyed in each mailing?

What mailing lists will be used?

Distribution Channels

What organizations will be included in the distribution network?

What role will each organization serve within the network?

Worksheet 14

Establishing Marketing Objectives

List the objectives associated with each marketing strategy and specify: (a) how the effectiveness of the objective in accomplishing the strategy will be measured (e.g., through an e-mail customer survey) and (b) the amount of change or outcome expected (e.g., 25% increase in customer satisfaction).

MARKETING STRATEGY:		
OBJECTIVES	**MEASURES**	**OUTCOME**
1.		
2.		
3.		
4.		
5.		

Worksheet 15

Creating an Implementation Plan

Below fill in the steps needed to implement each marketing tactic and next to each step, indicate the date of completion, the individual who will be responsible for overseeing the activity, the resources needed (e.g., software, consultant expertise) to complete the step and the associated costs.

TACTIC:				
STEPS	COMPLETION DATE	INDIVIDUAL RESPONSIBLE	RESOURCES NEEDED	COST
1.				
2.				
3.				
4.				
5.				
6.				
7.				
8.				
9.				
10.				

Worksheet 16

After you have prepared a draft marketing plan, review the document to ensure that it answers the following questions.

Target Market

- What are the general characteristics of the market and its various segments?
- What is the target market for the certification program and what is the rationale for the selection of this market?
- What are the demographics of the target market?
- What are customers' needs and motivations with respect to certification and other professional development activities?

Situational Analysis

- What are the organization's strengths and weaknesses with respect to marketing?
- What opportunities and threats are present within the marketplace?
- What is the nature of competition in the market?
- Who are the program's primary competitors and how do they operate their businesses?

Positioning and Marketing Strategies

- What makes the program distinctive vis-à-vis competitors?
- What customer needs/desires does the program satisfy?
- What is the desired positioning for the certification program and why?
- How do the marketing strategies capitalize on market opportunities and minimize market threats?
- How do the marketing strategies leverage competitive strengths and minimize competitive weaknesses?
- What are the objectives of the marketing strategies?
- What tactics will be used to implement the positioning and marketing strategies and how will their effectiveness be measured?

Implementation

- What steps will be taken to implement the marketing strategies and by what date must these activities be completed?
- Who will be responsible for overseeing the implementation of the plan and the marketing strategies?
- What resources are needed to implement the plan?
- What are the costs associated with implementing each strategy and the overall plan?

Worksheet 17

Developing the Program Vision

Answer the questions below and use the responses to guide you in developing the vision for the program.

Where will the program be 5–10 years from now?

What will make the program distinctive?

How will the program make a difference for certificants, stakeholders, and the profession/industry in general?

Craft a vision incorporating your answers to the preceding questions.

Worksheet 18

Determining What Products/Services Will Be Offered

The process of deciding which products/services to offer should be based on a thoughtful analysis of:

- market research findings;
- competitive analysis findings;
- the program's mission and business strategy; and
- the sponsoring organization's strengths and weaknesses.

This worksheet will guide you in conducting this analysis.

In Matrix 1, list unmet needs that exist within the target market. In the next column, identify new products and services or new features of existing products/services that might meet these needs.

Matrix 1

CUSTOMER NEED	NEW PRODUCT OR FEATURE	NEW SERVICE OR FEATURE
1.		
2.		
3.		
4.		

In Matrix 2, fill in each of the new products/services/features identified in Matrix 1. To the right, under the heading "Current Competitive Offerings," describe similar market offerings provided by competitors. If no similar offerings exist at present, write "None" in this section. In the next columns, rate the proposed product/service/feature along the following dimensions:

- *Distinctiveness.* How distinctive is the product/service/feature relative to existing offerings?
- *Competitive advantage.* To what degree will the product/service/feature provide a competitive advantage?
- *Feasibility.* How feasible would it be to provide the product/service/feature given the organization's strengths and weaknesses?
- *Support of vision and business strategy.* To what degree does the product/service/feature support the program's vision, business strategy, and overall strategic goals?

Use the following scale for your ratings:

1 Low
2 Moderate
3 High

— continued

Worksheet 18

Determining What Products/Services Will Be Offered (cont'd)

Matrix 2

NEW PRODUCT/ SERVICE/FEATURE	CURRENT COMPETITIVE OFFERINGS	DISTINCTIVENESS	COMPETITIVE ADVANTAGE	FEASIBILITY	SUPPORT OF VISION/STRATEGY

Worksheet 19

Outlining Operational Requirements

Use this worksheet to outline the operational requirements for maintaining the certification program and/or implementing the proposed changes.

Staff

List the positions required to staff the program and the full-time equivalencies (FTE) for each position.

POSITION	RESPONSIBILITIES	FTE

Vendors/Consultants

For each of the functional areas listed below, indicate whether a vendor/consultant will be used (by placing a check in the second column) and if so, specify the responsibilities that will be assigned to the vendor/consultant. Extra space has been provided in which to add other functional areas relevant to your program.

FUNCTIONAL AREA	VENDOR/ CONSULTANT	RESPONSIBILITIES
Examination development		
Application processing		
Examination administration		
Information technology		
Web site		
Graphic design		
Legal		
Accounting		

— continued

Worksheet 19

Outlining Operational Requirements (cont'd)

Volunteers

Below list the purpose of the board/oversight committee and each program committee and indicate the number of volunteers needed. Extra space has been provided in which to add other committees and task forces relevant to your program.

	RESPONSIBILITIES	# PERSONS
Board/oversight committee	______________________	________
Examination development	______________________	________
Eligibility	______________________	________
Appeals	______________________	________
Marketing	______________________	________
____________	______________________	________

Facilities and Equipment

Office space

Below specify the desired size and location of office space and specific features required (e.g., private offices, conference room).

Size ______________________

Location ______________________

Features ______________________

____

Office equipment

List standard office equipment, hardware, and software needed to support the program.

____

____

____

Specialized hardware/software

List specialized hardware/software needed to support the program (e.g., optical scanner for answer sheets, question analysis software).

____

____

____

Security equipment, systems, and software

List equipment, systems, and software needed to maintain the security of the program's databases and electronic and paper files.

____

____

____

____

Worksheet 20

Formulating Revenue and Expense Projections

To derive five-year revenue and expense projections, insert into the spreadsheet below your revenue and expense estimates.

FIVE-YEAR PROJECTION OF INCOME AND EXPENSE

	Year 1	Year 2	Year 3	Year 4	Year 5
REVENUES					
Start-up Funding					
Certification Revenue					
Other Income					
TOTAL REVENUES	**$**	**$**	**$**	**$**	**$**
EXPENSES					
General & Administrative Expenses					
Marketing					
Program Development					
Program Delivery Expense					
TOTAL EXPENSES	**$**	**$**	**$**	**$**	**$**
NET INCOME (LOSS)	**$**	**$**	**$**	**$**	**$**

Worksheet 21

Business Plan Checklist

After you have prepared a draft business plan, review the document to ensure that it answers the following questions.

Market Analysis

- What is the target market?
- What are the characteristics of the target market (e.g., demographics, needs/desires)?
- How does the certification program satisfy customers' needs and desires?
- What environmental factors impact this market?

Competitive Analysis

- Who are the program's direct and indirect competitors?
- What are the competitors' strengths and weaknesses?
- What customers are competitors targeting?
- On what basis do competitors compete (e.g., price, quality, prestige, access, convenience)?
- How will they respond to the program's entry into the market?
- What competitive opportunities and threats exist?
- How will the program respond to these opportunities and threats?

Competitive Strategy

- What are the program's primary competitive advantages and how can the program capitalize on these?
- What are the program's primary competitive weaknesses and how will the program overcome or minimize these?
- What are the most critical features that distinguish the program from its competition?
- What specific steps will be taken to implement the competitive strategy?

Products/Services

- What products/services will the program offer?
- How do these products/services differ from those of competitors?
- What additional products/services will most likely be offered in the future?

Marketing

- What is the desired positioning for the program?
- What messages/themes will be used in marketing the program?
- What strategies will be used to accomplish marketing goals?
- How do the marketing strategies relate to the competitive strategy?

Worksheet 21

Business Plan Checklist (cont'd)

Program Operations

- What entity or entities will administer the program?
- Who are the key staff and what related experience do they bring to the program?
- What operations are necessary to provide the products/services in the manner outlined in the business plan?
- What facilities and equipment are needed?

Financial Data

- What will be the fees for the products/services offered?
- What is the anticipated volume for the first year of the program? For subsequent years?
- What are the budgets for program development and maintenance?
- What is the break-even point?
- What are the revenue and expense projections?
- Will cash flow be adequate?
- What assumptions have been made in formulating the financial data?